My Book

Our loving God
    Created Heaven and earth.
And, in His wisdom,
    Let life begin in Spring.

Let plants and living creatures
    Grow in Summer,
Let Autumn be a time
        For harvesting.

Then God created Winter,
    One more season,
And let it be a time
        For all to rest.

Each season has its purpose,
    Each one different.
But all the seasons
    Of the year are blessed.

THE LITTLE APPLE TREE

Words and pictures by dolli tingle

Stardust Books

THE C. R. GIBSON COMPANY
Publishers
NORWALK, CONNECTICUT

It's Spring!
And in the sunny April meadow
The apple tree
Wears flowers, pink and white.

The air is filled
With apple blossom petals.
And bees buzz...
Dizzy at the lovely sight.

Two robins build their nest
High up in the branches.
They weave it snug and strong
With twigs and string.

And Mother Rabbit
Leaves her Winter burrow.
She brings her bunnies out
To greet the Spring.

And now, in light green leaves
All new and shining,
The little apple tree
Is gaily dressed.

Up in the leafy branches
Mrs. Robin
Keeps four blue eggs warm
Deep inside the nest.

Soon fuzzy baby birds
Have sprouted feathers.
They lift their little wings
And fly away.

Then children out of school
Run to the meadow.
To climb up in the apple tree
And play.

The children point
And call out to each other.
What is it?
What do all the childen see?

On every branch
A tiny, hard, green apple grows
Where once a pale pink blossom
Used to be.

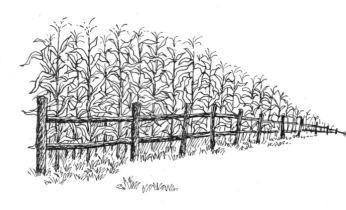

For this is Summer.
Days are hot and sunny.
The season meant for growing
Has begun.

The apples grow
And so do all the children.
They grow while playing
In the Summer sun.

When Summer ends
The children leave the meadow.
Cool, crisp October days
Lie just ahead.

And look!
The little apple tree is wearing
A fancy gown
With polka dots of red.

For it is Autumn
  And harvest time is here.
  The apples have grown
  Rosy, round and big.
  The farmer brings his ladder
  To the meadow
  And picks the apples
  Hanging from each twig.

One day the winds blow cold.
The sky is cloudy.
Each leaf upon the tree
Comes fluttering down.

The birds fly south
For soon it will be winter.
The grass beneath the tree
Turns dry and brown.

December!
Now the apple tree is sleeping.
And snowflakes,
Drifting down from overhead,

Will spread a soft white blanket
On its branches
To keep it cozy
In its winter bed.

The Winter is a
Quiet restful season
When trees and flowers sleep
Beneath the snow,

When lonely rabbits
  Scamper through the meadow,
And leave their tracks
  To mark the way they go.

On one bright morning
  In the wintry meadow
 The sun shines warm
 And melts the snow away.

The little apple tree
Awakes from sleeping.
The birds come back.
New baby bunnies play.

It's Spring again !
Another new beginning.
The apple tree
Wears flowers, pink and white.
The air is filled
With apple blossom petals
And bees buzz...
Dizzy at the lovely sight.